First published 2010 by Walker Books Ltd
87 Vauxhall Walk, London SE11 5HJ

2 4 6 8 10 9 7 5 3 1

Printed and bound in Italy

British Library Cataloguing in Publication Data:
a catalogue record for this book is available from the British Library

ISBN 978-1-4063-2050-3

www.walker.co.uk

www.andiwatson.biz

for
Mum & Dad

Glister's Mum

Janet Butterworth

Poldie

faerie guide

Brae Burn

Helpful faerie

KING
of the
Faerie Host

Now, there was one thing that Glister held precious above all other things.

Her hoody.

It had been knitted for her by her mother. No matter how many times she washed it, carefully, by hand, it always smelt of her mum.

Whenever she put the cardigan on, it felt like being held close to her mother's chest as a baby. The memory of warm skin against her cheek and her mother's hair falling over her face engulfed her.

The lulling scent of Earl Grey tea and lavender.

It was clear that Glister's mother had knitted something of herself into the garment because, although it had been made for a baby, it always fitted Glister as she grew.

Glister knew why her father tried to make each Christmas more magical than the last. It was because he could never give her the one present she truly wished for.

Her mum.

Glister's mother was soon lost and stuck in the snow.

She sought shelter in an orchard, curling under an apple tree in an attempt to keep warm.

It was there that she fell into a deep sleep.

JANET
BUTTERWORTH

mum?

≶SOB≶

Without explaining what Glister had seen in the mirror, she dragged her father to the church in Gravehunger Moss. The exact same churchyard she'd chased her mother to in the mirror not long before.

I don't understand how or why someone would do this.

That night, Glister couldn't shake off the feeling that there was something oddly familiar about the crude stick figure dug out of the ground.

She decided to take a closer look before her dad tossed it onto the fire.

It smelled like her mother.

The hair...it's mum's.

Carrying her silver potato peeler and wearing the closest she had to a mantle, Glister stepped over the border.

Which way to the King's court... thingymajig?
I go by the name of Poldie, sapling. Now, follow y'nose and look sharp. Shilly shally longer and y' mother will be lost forever.
Glister ran until her lungs were raw. The figure of her mother danced just out of reach in her mind, urging her forward.
Then she could go no further.

What Should I do, Poldie? It's too far to swim.
Look under y'nose.
Glister's mother had sewn three buttons onto her daughter's hoody. One of wood, one of bone and one of iron.
Glister pulled off the wooden button.
Y'waitin' for it t'sprout wings, lassie?
Into the water.
When the button hit the water it transformed into a coracle.

Glister followed her nose until she realized it was leading her around in circles.

I admit I'm lost.

No use in lookin' at me, I can't aid ye, but Hindlip might be persuaded.

Where's Hindlip?

It seemed to her that Faerieland was a single orchard sprawling identically in all directions, without a landmark to be seen.
Glister was soon lost again.
Hindlip's tricked us. This way's no better than any other.
I can't aid ye, but Brae Burn might be persuaded.
Where's Brae Burn?
What would y' be wanting Brae Burn for?

Skip widdershins three times around the mound.

Glister guessed where the sun might be, although it never showed itself in Faerieland, and skipped in the opposite direction.

As Glister completed her third turn, the entrance revealed itself.

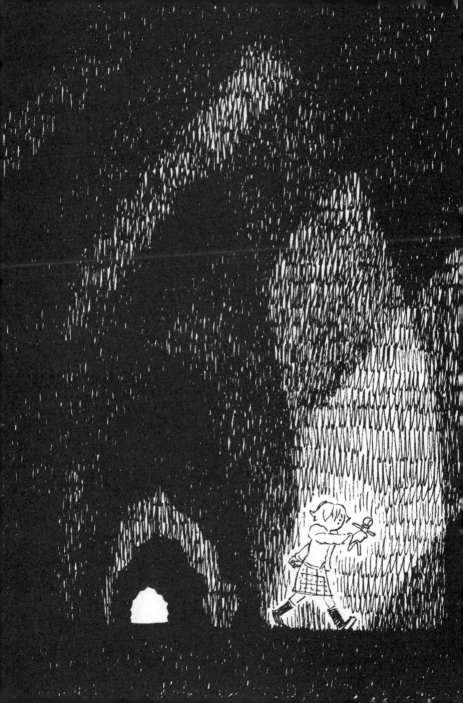

Poldie directed Glister deeper and deeper into the earth. She tried not to think about how lost she would be without her guide.

Eventually, Glister was lead through a confused knot of warrens that ended in a grand, hollowed-out hall.

His majesty makes more promises than he keeps. Look sharp and keep y'r wits about y'.

Having safely paddled back across the oily river, Glister sent the tiny boat back to her mother.

The King kept his promise, if not his word, and swept the coracle away.

Time had flown differently in Faerie and, at Chilblain Hall, it was already Christmas.

Chilblain was still standing, as was Glister's father, who'd gone out searching every day since she'd disappeared.

For the first time in many years, it was a merry Christmas at Chilblain Hall.

THE END

Andi Watson grew up in a small town in West Yorkshire. It's a nice place but a bit dull so he watched too much telly, read a lot and enjoyed filling blank sheets of paper with drawings of space battles. He's always loved stories, drawing and books so when he re-discovered comics while at art school he found he'd stumbled on the perfect way to combine all the things he likes to do. What he enjoys most about *Glister* is the freedom to create any kind of story and follow funny ideas wherever they lead.

Some of his favourite things are: Hayao Miyazaki films, cake, cups of tea, second-hand book shops, depressing music, brussels sprouts, chocolate, long-tailed tits and fairy tales.

Andi has been nominated for the prestigious Eisner Award and Harvey Award which both recognize outstanding works in comics and sequential art.

He's worked in a variety of genres, from sci-fi and fantasy to contemporary drama, romantic comedy and now stories for children.

He lives in Worcester with his wife and daughter. *Glister* is his first series for Walker Books.

www.andiwatson.biz